MORNING ·BELLS·

P. David Pearson   Dale D. Johnson

Theodore Clymer   Roselmina Indrisano   Richard L. Venezky

James F. Baumann   Elfrieda Hiebert   Marian Toth

Consulting Authors

Carl Grant   Jeanne Paratore

SILVER BURDETT & GINN

NEEDHAM, MA • MORRISTOWN, NJ

ATLANTA, GA • CINCINNATI, OH • DALLAS, TX

MENLO PARK, CA • NORTHFIELD, IL

Contents

The Hokeypokey 4
Sing with Me

That's What It's All About! 8
Photo Essay

Play Mittens 12
Real-Life Story

Hokeypokey One and All 22
Make-Believe Story

Rhyme Time 32
Learning About Rhyming

Brother John 34
Sing with Me

Who Is It ? 38
Photo Essay

A Gift for Uncle Bill 42
Real-Life Story

Time for Brother John 52
Make-Believe Story

What Will Go In ? 62
Learning About Classification

The World of Reading: **Make a Book** . . . 64
Making Word Books

Year Round the Raindrops 66
Read with Me
by Bill Martin Jr and John Archambault
Pictures by Lois Ehlert

Dictionary 80

The Hokeypokey

You put your left hand in.
You take your left hand out.
You put your left hand in,
and you shake it all about.

You do the hokeypokey,
and you turn yourself around.
That's what it's all about.

You put your right hand in.
You take your right hand out.
You put your right hand in,
and you shake it all about.

You do the hokeypokey,
and you turn yourself around.
That's what it's all about.

You put your left foot in.
You take your left foot out.
You put your left foot in,
and you shake it all about.

You do the hokeypokey,
and you turn yourself around.
That's what it's all about.

You put your right foot in.
You take your right foot out.
You put your right foot in,
and you shake it all about.

You do the hokeypokey,
and you turn yourself around.
That's what it's all about.

That's What It's All About!

He will jump in.

His left foot will go up and down.

His right foot will, too.

His feet will go up and down.

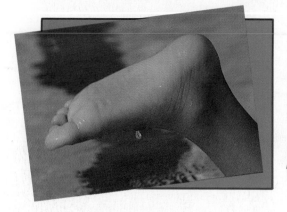

His left hand will go in and out.

His right hand will, too.

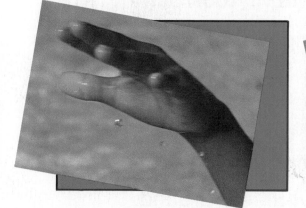

What is it all about?

She will turn with her left hand.

He will turn with his right hand.

It's her turn.

Her feet jump up and down.

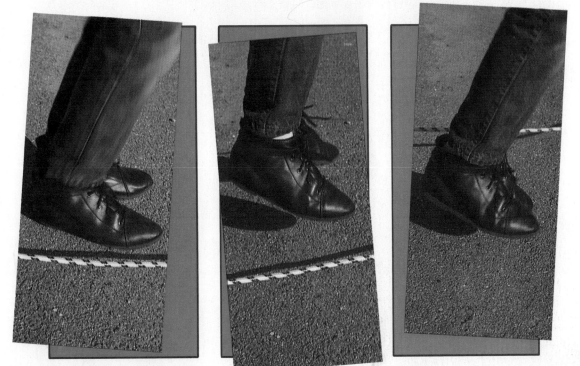

What is it all about?

She will hop on her right foot.

She will hop and hop and jump.

She will turn around.

She will hop on her left foot.

What is it all about?

That's right !
That's what it's all about !

Play Mittens

Jane went up to Mr. Bell.
"I found this blue mitten.
I did not find the other one.
Can you find out who lost it?"
she said.

"Jane, you can hold up the
blue mitten. Find out who
lost it," said Mr. Bell.

"I found this mitten. Who lost
a blue mitten?" said Jane.

"It is not my mitten. I have
my mittens right here," said Bob.

"Is this your mitten, Pat?"
said Jane.

"No, I have my mittens, too,"
said Pat.

"No one has lost a mitten,"
said Jane.

"I can put it in the lost and
found box," said Mr. Bell.

"Look at all the mittens!"
said Jane.

"No one came for the mittens in this box," said Mr. Bell.

"Can I have one of the mittens?" said Jane.

"What can you do with one lost mitten?" said Bob.

"I can make a hand puppet like this one. You can make one, too," said Jane.

"I like Jane's plan. I will give you all a lost mitten. You can all make a mitten puppet like Jane's puppet," said Mr. Bell.

"My puppet is K.C. Bear,"
said Jane. She put her right hand
in her puppet.

"My puppet is D.D. Bear,"
said Pat. She put her left hand
in her puppet.

"You and I can make up
a play about the Bears who live
in a cave. You and I can sing
about the Bears," said Jane.

"My puppet is Bingo, the dog.
I will make up a play about
a naughty dog. I will sing about
Bingo," said Fran.

"My puppet is Bitsy. I can
sing about Bitsy," said Tim.

"This is Nat. You and I can
put on a play about Bitsy and Nat.
I can sing with you," said Bob.

"Help me fix the big box for the puppet play," said Mr. Bell.

"I can fix one side of the box," said Tim.

"I can fix the other side of the box," said Fran.

It was Jane's turn to give
her play. Jane and Pat put on
a play about the Bears who live
in a cave.

"What a lot of fun this is!
Give Jane and Pat a big hand!"
said Mr. Bell.

Hokeypokey One and All

Becky and Mike went to skate.

"We will have fun. We will sing and skate the hokeypokey," said Becky.

"The hokeypokey looks like fun," said Mike.

"Get in line and skate with me.
It's time for the hokeypokey,"
said Becky.

"Here we go!" said Mike.

All the others put a left hand in. All the others put a left hand out.

Mike put his right hand in and his right hand out.

"Do the hokeypokey! Turn around and clap," said Becky.

All the others put a right hand in. They put a right hand out.

This time, Mike put his left hand in and his left hand out.

All the others put a left
foot in. They put a left foot out.

Mike put his right foot in and
his right foot out.

All the others put a right
foot in. They put a right foot out.

This time, Mike did not put
his foot in. He put his foot down.
He did not turn around and clap.
He did not do the hokeypokey.

"I can't do it right!"
said Mike.

"I can help you. I will put
one ribbon on your right skate.
I will put one ribbon on your
right hand," said Becky.

"I get it. Red is for my
right side. My right hand has
a red ribbon. My right foot
has a red ribbon," said Mike.

"That's right!" said Becky.

"We can get back in line.
It's time to sing and skate
the hokeypokey," said Mike.

Mike and Becky went back
in line. All the others went
back in line, too.

This time Mike did the
hokeypokey like all the others.
He did it right all the time.

"The hokeypokey is fun
to do!" said Mike.

Rhyme Time

Brother John

Are you sleeping ?

Are you sleeping ?

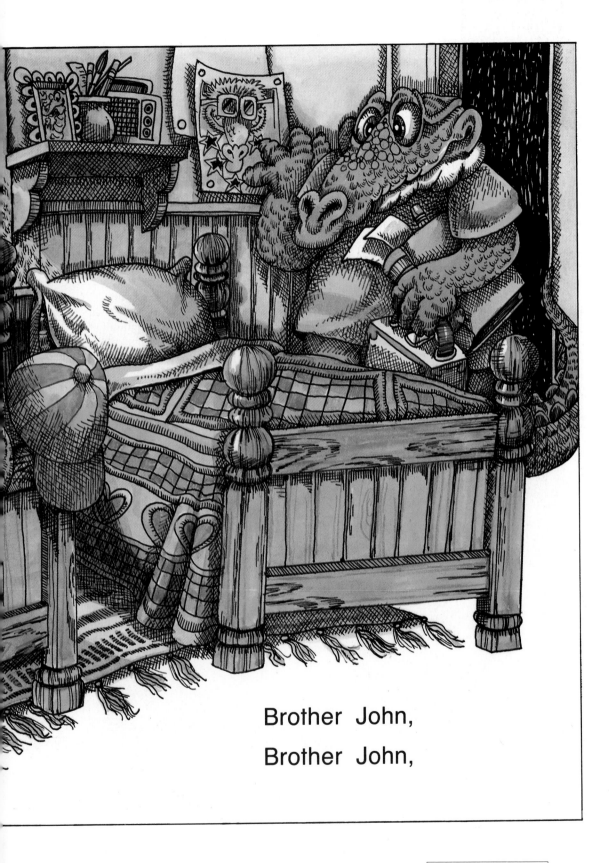

Brother John,

Brother John,

Morning bells are ringing!
Morning bells are ringing!

♪ Sing With Me

Who Is It?

Who can have a brother?

A sister can have a brother.
A brother can have a brother.

Who can have a brother?

A mother can have a brother.
A father can have a brother.

Who can have a sister?

A brother can have a sister.
A sister can have a sister.

Who can have a sister?

A father can have a sister.
A mother can have a sister.

A Gift for Uncle Bill

Lee did not have a gift for Uncle Bill. It was his birthday.

"Dad, do I have time to make Uncle Bill a gift?" said Lee.

"Yes, you have time to make him a gift," said Father.

"I do not know what to give him," said Lee.

Lee went to her brother for help. "I do not know what to make for Uncle Bill," said Lee.

"Make him a cap like this one," said Dave.

"I do not know how to make a cap. No, a cap will not do," said Lee.

Lee went to her sister
for help. "What could I make
for Uncle Bill?" said Lee.

"You could make mittens
for him," said Kit.

"I do not know how to make
mittens. I know! I can make a
book for him," said Lee.

Lee went to her mother for
help. "Uncle Bill will like a book.
Could you help me make a book
for him?" said Lee.

"Yes, I will help you. I know
how to make a book," said Mother.

"What will you put in the book?"
said Mother.

"I can put pictures I like in the
book," said Lee.

Father handed a box of pictures to Lee.

"Look in this box. Find the pictures you like. Put the pictures in your book," said Father.

"I know how to put pictures in a book!" said Lee.

"Can we put pictures in the book, too?" said Dave and Kit.

"Yes, find the pictures you like," said Lee.

"I am so happy we can all make a gift for Uncle Bill," said Lee.

"So am I," said Mother.

"I put a ribbon around the book so it looks like a gift," said Lee.

"Here is Uncle Bill!" said Kit.

"Get down so we can surprise him!" said Dave.

"Happy birthday, Uncle Bill!
This gift is for you," said Lee.
She handed him the gift.

"I like this birthday gift a lot!
I like my book," said Uncle Bill.

Time for Brother John

"John! Max! It's morning.
It's time to go to school,"
said Mother.

"It's not late. I have a lot
of time," said John.

John went back to sleep.
His brother Max went to school.

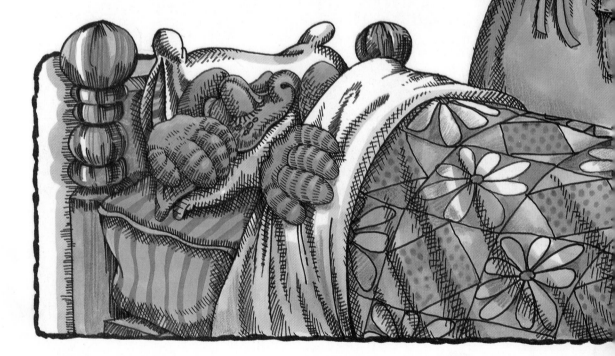

"John, get up! It's time
to go to school. You are late,"
said Mother.

"Am I late, Mother?"
said John.

"The school bell is ringing.
You are late," said Mother.

"John, you are late. Will you try to get to school on time?" said Mrs. Gator.

"I will try, Mrs. Gator," said John.

"You do not get up on time. You have to try," said Max.

"I know. I try to get up on time. I like to sleep in the morning," said John.

"John, you have to get up on time!" said Max.

"I know! I know!" said John.

It was morning. John did not get up on time. He went back to sleep.

"John, are you sleeping?"
said Max.

"Yes, I am sleeping," said John.

"It's time to get up," said Max.

"I said I am sleeping,"
said John.

"I know how to get you up for
school. I will clap so you will get
up," said Max.

"Do not clap! I will get up,"
said John.

"No, no! The school bell is
ringing. We are late! I could not
get you up on time!" said Max.

"You are late, John. Max, you are late, too," said Mrs. Gator.

"Mrs. Gator, I did try to get John to school on time. I could not do it," said Max.

"So I see. You did get here in time for fun. It's time to go down to the water. Get in line with the others," said Mrs. Gator.

"Mrs. Gator, are you ringing?" said Max.

"I am not ringing. This clock is ringing. Time is up!" said Mrs. Gator. She handed the clock to Max.

"I know what to do. I will give John a clock," said Max.

"Give it a try!" said Mrs. Gator.

It was morning. Mother did not go to get John. Max did not go to get John.

The bell on the clock was ringing. John went to look for the ringing clock.

"Are you sleeping, Brother John?" said Max.

"No, I am not sleeping. I can't sleep with this clock ringing," said John.

"Sleeping time is up!" said Max.

"The ringing clock will get me up so I will not go back to sleep. This late gator will get to school on time!" said John.

What Will Go In?

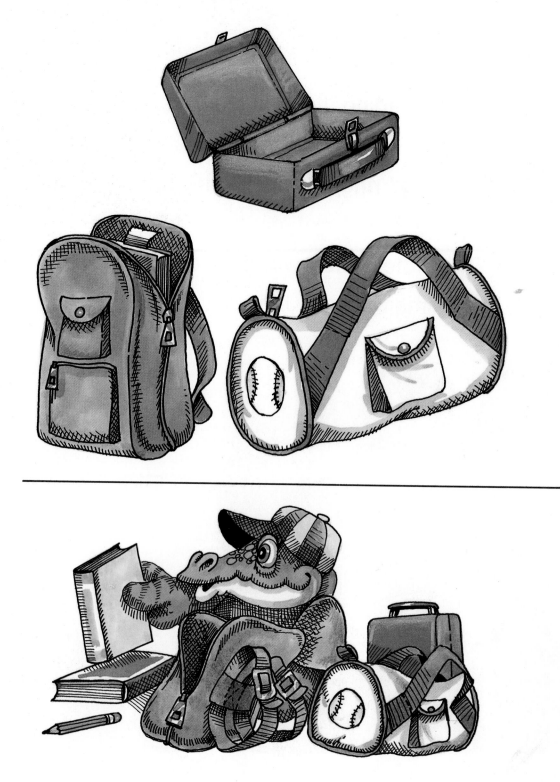

1.

2.

3.

4.

Make a Book

Fun Words

mushy

squishy

poodles

giggle

watermelon
peanut butter
spaghetti

batter up
shortstop
stadium

Year Round the Raindrops

by Bill Martin Jr and John Archambault

Read With Me

In the early spring,

do the raindrops sing,

📖 Read With Me

as they drippy-drop-drip

from the tippy-top-tip

and trickle down the branches

of the pear tree?

On the 4th of July
as the raindrops fly,
are they red-white-and-blue?

Do they Yankee doodle do?

Do they boom, do they bang,

and sparkle, too,

like we do?

When vacation ends
and school begins,

Read With Me

do the raindrops cry
when they say good-bye
to the places they've been
in summer?

📖 **Read With Me**

When winter comes
and numbs the thumbs,
do the raindrops quake?
Do they shiver, do they shake?

  **Read With Me**

Do they know they'll soon be
snowflakes?

Dictionary

about

The book is **about** dogs.

are

The puppies **are** tan.

back

Come **back** here, Kit!

birthday

It is my **birthday**.

book

This **book** is good.

box

The cap is in the **box**.

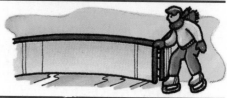

brother

My **brother** will skate.

clap

He can **clap**.

clock

Look at the **clock**.

father

Here is my **father**.

feet

His **feet** are big.

foot

I put my **foot** here.

found

I **found** a mitten.

gift

She has a **gift**.

give

Max, **give** it to me.

hand

    I put my **hand** up.

her

    Bob is **her** brother.

him

    I can see **him**.

his

    Kit is **his** cat.

hop

    We like to **hop**.

how

    I do not know **how**.

know

    I **know** the time.

late

    He is sleeping **late**.

left

This is my **left** hand.

line

We skate in **line**.

lost

I **lost** my book.

mitten

I have one **mitten**.

mittens

Mom has **mittens**.

morning

It is **morning**.

mother

Here is my **mother**.

no

Mom said **no**.

one

I have **one** brother.

pictures

Look at my **pictures**.

puppet

I like the **puppet**.

ribbon

The **ribbon** is red.

right

This is my **right** hand.

ringing

The clock is **ringing**.

school

I go to **school**.

sing

I can **sing**.

sister

My **sister** will clap.

skate

I like to **skate**.

sleep

He will go to **sleep**.

sleeping

They are **sleeping**.

time

What **time** is it?

try

He will **try**.

turn

It's her **turn**.

yes

Mom said **yes**.

WORD LIST

The following words appear in *Morning Bells.* The words are listed next to the number of the page on which they first appear. Words with * are words that children can decode independently.

That's What It's All About

8 that's
it's
about
his
left
foot
right
feet*
hand

9 she
turn
her

10 hop*

Play Mittens

12 mittens
Mr.
Bell
found
blue
mitten
one
lost

13 Pat*
no*

14 box*

16 puppet
Jane's*
give

17 sing*

Hokeypokey One and All

22 hokeypokey
Becky
Mike*
skate
we *

23 line*
time*

24 others
clap*

28 ribbon

29 back*

Who Is It?

38 brother
sister

39 mother
father

A Gift for Uncle Bill

42 gift
Uncle
Bill
Lee*
birthday

43 yes*
him*
know

44 how
Dave*

45 Kit*
book

47 pictures

48 handed

49 so*

Time for Brother John

52 John
Max*
morning
school
late*
sleep

53 are
ringing

54 try
Mrs.
Gator

56 sleeping

59 clock*

Acknowledgments

Stories by Ann Martin Miranda and Mary Jane Martin
Design and Production in cooperation with Kirchoff/Wohlberg, Inc.
Cover Design by Design Five; Illustration by Dorothy Scott

Artists

Maxie Chambliss, pp. 4–7, 22–33; Lois Ehlert, pp. 66–79; Dara Goldman, pp. 42–51; Ron LeHew, pp. 34–37, 52–63; Diane Paterson, pp. 12–21; Lou Vaccaro, Dictionary.

Photographers

8–11, Lawrence Migdale; 38–41, Bob Daemmrich; 64–65 (background photo and circular inserts), Ken Karp, OPC; 65(t), Victoria Beller Smith; 65(b), Bob Daemmrich.

E F G H I J—RRD—96 95 94 93 92 91 90 89